Usborne Little Wipe-Clean
Word Book
About Me

Illustrated by Marta Cabrol

Designed by Yasmin Faulkner
Edited by Felicity Brooks

head

Trace over all
the words in
this book.

arm

leg

foot

My face

eye   ear

mouth   nose

hair   chin

My body

head

leg

hand

arm

foot

tummy

What I can do

run

dance

read

write

laugh

think

Things I wear

top

shorts

shirt

hat

socks

shoes

coat dress

sweater skirt

jeans gloves

My home

sofa

chair

bed

lamp

bathtub

toilet

stove   shower

table   rug

sink   window

My things

bike   doll

book   bear

truck   paints

My day

get up   dress

eat   play

wash   sleep

In my town

store

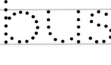
bus

car

bench

van

taxi

school   road

sun   cloud

tree   train

What I eat and drink

fruit   meat

vegetables

bread   salad

juice   milk

fish   pasta

cheese   water

At the park

slide

kite

swings

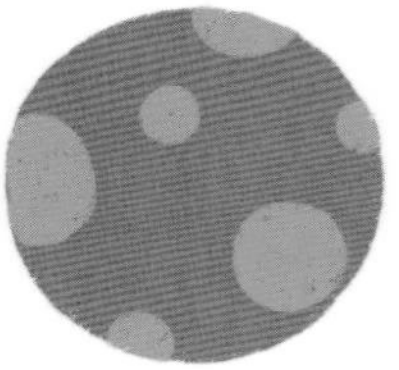

ball

seesaw

bat

At the café

burger hot dog

fries pizza

cake ice cream

Who I know

mom

dad

sister

brother

baby

cousin

cat   grandad

granny   dog

aunt   uncle

What I feel

happy   sad

proud   worried

shy   excited

cold   hot

hungry thirsty

sick   well

USBORNE

Usborne Little Wipe-Cl...
Word Book
About Me

This fun book is a perfect way for young children to improve their language and writing skills by tracing over 120 everyday words.

For advice about helping young children learn to read and write, and links to fun activities, go to www.usborne.com/quicklinks and enter the keywords "Early years activities."

www.edcpub.com or
www.usbornebooksandmore.com

Educational
Development
Corporation

Published in the USA by EDC PUBLISHING
5402 S. 122nd E. Avenue, Tulsa, Oklahoma 74146, USA.

NOT FOR SALE OUTSIDE OF THE USA

$6.99

JFMAMJJA OND/20 05426/3
Made with paper from a sustainable source.

ISBN 978-0-7945-4753-0

9 780794 547530 >

⚠ **WARNING:**
CHOKING HAZARD—Small parts.
Not for children under 3 yrs.

Ink from pen may not be washable.
This product conforms to ASTM D 4236.